MOBY DICK

**A GRAPHIC CLASSIC BY
TERRY M. WEST**

**BASED ON THE NOVEL BY
HERMAN MELVILLE**

SCHOLASTIC INC.
New York Toronto London Auckland Sydney
Mexico City New Delhi Hong Kong

PENCILLER
RYAN DUNLAVEY

INKER
RICH PERROTTA

COLORIST
J. BROWN AND TECH FX

LETTERER
JON OOSTING

COVER ARTIST
MICHAEL LILLY

COVER COLORS
J. BROWN AND TECH FX

Copyright © 1999 by Scholastic Inc.
All rights reserved. Published by Scholastic Inc.
Printed in the U.S.A.

ISBN 0-439-05671-3

SCHOLASTIC, READ 180, and associated logos and designs are trademarks and/or registered trademarks of Scholastic Inc.
LEXILE is a trademark of MetaMetrics, Inc.

2   3   4   5   6   7   8   9   10   23   06 05 04 03 02 01 00 99

MOBY DICK

*T*HE YEAR WAS 1837, AND 18-YEAR-OLD HERMAN MELVILLE NEEDED WORK. LIKE MANY MEN HIS AGE, HE SIGNED ON WITH A WHALING SHIP IN NEW ENGLAND.

SAILORS ON SUCH EXPEDITIONS SPENT UP TO TWO YEARS HUNTING WHALES. BACK ON THE MAINLAND, BONES FROM WHALES WERE USED FOR FISHING RODS AND UMBRELLAS. WHALE OIL WAS TURNED INTO CANDLES, FUEL FOR LAMPS—AND EVEN EXPENSIVE PERFUMES.

THE SAILING LIFE SUITED MELVILLE, AND HE WENT TO SEA MANY TIMES. IN 1850, HE PUBLISHED A NOVEL BASED ON HIS ADVENTURES. AT THE TIME, PEOPLE DIDN'T THINK MUCH OF HIS BOOK, CALLED <u>MOBY DICK</u>, BUT IT IS NOW CONSIDERED AN AMERICAN CLASSIC.

ISHMAEL HAD BEEN A SCHOOLTEACHER FOR MOST OF HIS SHORT ADULT LIFE. IT WAS NOW TIME TO SEE THE WORLD.

NO GREATER ADVENTURE COULD BE HAD THAN ON A WHALING SHIP. HE WOULD FIND A SHIP TO SIGN ON WITH, HERE IN NANTUCKET. ISHMAEL WAS ANXIOUS TO SEE WHAT AWAITED HIM BEYOND THE SHORES OF NANTUCKET.

ISHMAEL DECIDED TO FIND A PLACE TO SPEND THE NIGHT.

TOMORROW HE WOULD FIND A SHIP TO SIGN ON WITH.

HE MANAGED TO FIND A ROOM.

AT DINNER, HE MET A MAN NAMED QUEEQUEG.

QUEEQUEG WAS ONE OF THE BEST HARPOONERS IN THE WHALING BUSINESS.

You will be my shipmate, Ishmael. I will teach you all I know of whaling.

EARLY THE NEXT MORNING, ISHMAEL AND QUEEQUEG SOUGHT A WHALING SHIP TO SIGN ON WITH.

You pick. They all look the same to me.

SHIPOWNERS USUALLY PICKED THE CREW FOR THE WHALING EXPEDITIONS. BUSINESSMEN PAID FOR THE SHIPS AND SOLD THE OIL THAT THE CREW WOULD RETURN WITH.

We'd like to sign on, sir.

Do you have any experience?

No, but ...

We are only hiring experienced seamen.

Don't be hasty.

Look at his shipmate. He's an expert harpooner if I've ever seen one.

Very well. Welcome to the crew of the *Pequod.*

But you will only receive a fraction of your shipmate's salary.

Fair enough.

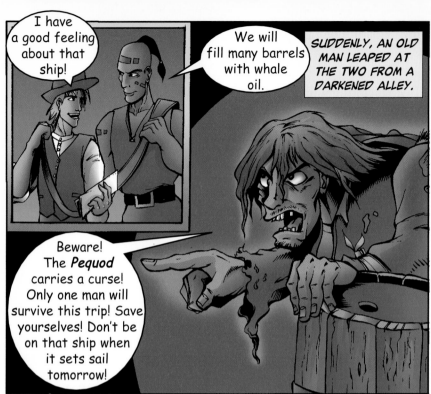

I have a good feeling about that ship!

We will fill many barrels with whale oil.

SUDDENLY, AN OLD MAN LEAPED AT THE TWO FROM A DARKENED ALLEY.

Beware! The *Pequod* carries a curse! Only one man will survive this trip! Save yourselves! Don't be on that ship when it sets sail tomorrow!

What was that all about?

That was Elijah. Don't pay any attention to him. He says that to many seamen before they board their ships. He's just trying to scare you.

He did a good job.

THE NEXT MORNING ISHMAEL AND QUEEQUEG BOARDED THE *PEQUOD* AND WERE OFF.

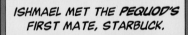

ISHMAEL MET THE *PEQUOD'S* FIRST MATE, STARBUCK.

STARBUCK WAS IN CHARGE OF CARRYING OUT THE CAPTAIN'S ORDERS AND ASSIGNING JOBS TO THE CREW.

BECAUSE OF ISHMAEL'S INEXPERIENCE, STARBUCK GAVE HIM THE JOB OF SWABBING THE DECKS.

Not a bad day's work for a landlubber.

We'll make a sailor out of you yet.

Aye, I would like that.

Give it a few days, lad. After the rope-burns, dry skin, and sea sickness, you'll miss the land more than you think.

ISHMAEL AND THE REST OF THE CREW RELAXED FOR A FEW MOMENTS AS THE WIND CHARGED THE *PEQUOD'S* SAILS. THE *PEQUOD'S* SECOND MATE, STUBBS, TOOK A MOMENT TO SPEAK WITH ISHMAEL.

Those are small prices to pay for adventure.

But tell me, what about the captain? I haven't seen him since we set sail.

Captain Ahab is down below in his quarters.

He's plotting our course.

DAYS ON THE *PEQUOD* PASSED, AS THE SHIP SAILED ON AND ON.

THE MYSTERIOUS AHAB HAD NOT BEEN SEEN BY THE CREW. ISHMAEL WONDERED OFTEN ABOUT THE CAPTAIN.

SOMETIMES IT TOOK WEEKS FOR WHALING SHIPS TO SPOT WHALES.

ISHMAEL HOPED THE *PEQUOD* WOULD RUN ACROSS THEM SOON.

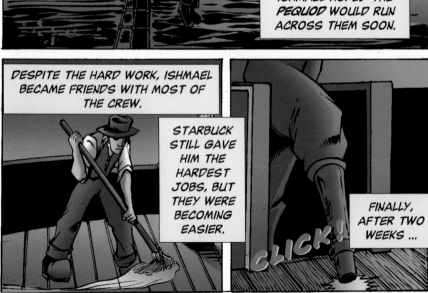

DESPITE THE HARD WORK, ISHMAEL BECAME FRIENDS WITH MOST OF THE CREW.

STARBUCK STILL GAVE HIM THE HARDEST JOBS, BUT THEY WERE BECOMING EASIER.

CLICK!

FINALLY, AFTER TWO WEEKS ...

AT ATTENTION! CAPTAIN ON DECK!!!

CLICK!

CLICK!

Psst! Eyes forward, lad!

Behold, men. A Spanish gold coin.

It's worth a handsome price.

WHOEVER AMONG YOU KILLS THE WHITE WHALE SHALL HAVE THIS GOLD OUNCE!

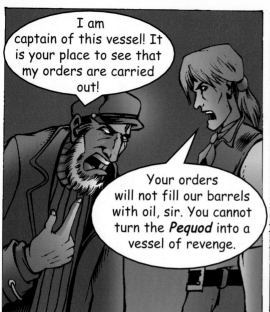

For that ounce of gold, I would hunt Neptune himself!

Don't waste your time! The white whale will fall to *my* harpoon!

AHAB'S SPEECH FRIGHTENED AND INTRIGUED ISHMAEL AT THE SAME TIME.

TO KILL A LEGEND SUCH AS MOBY DICK WOULD MAKE THE *PEQUOD* AND ITS CREW FAMOUS, BUT ISHMAEL OFTEN THOUGHT OF AHAB'S PEG LEG AND SHUDDERED.

ISHMAEL COULD TELL THAT STARBUCK WANTED NO PART OF AHAB'S QUEST. BUT STARBUCK WAS A FAITHFUL FIRST MATE. HE HAD TO OBEY AHAB'S WISHES.

Ahab is the captain of this ship. We will follow his orders ... even if they lead to a watery grave!

SECOND MATE STUBBS HAD NO PROBLEM CARRYING OUT AHAB'S ORDERS. HE WAS ACTUALLY LOOKING FORWARD TO THE CHALLENGE OF CHASING MOBY DICK.

ISHMAEL DISCOVERED THAT AHAB HAD PUT TOGETHER A CRUDE MAP BASED ON THE SIGHTINGS OF THE WHITE WHALE. THE **PEQUOD** WAS FOLLOWING A PATH THAT AHAB HAD BEEN PIECING TOGETHER FOR YEARS—A PATH THAT AHAB HOPED WOULD LEAD TO MOBY DICK.

DO YOU SEE THE WHITE WHALE AMONG THEM?

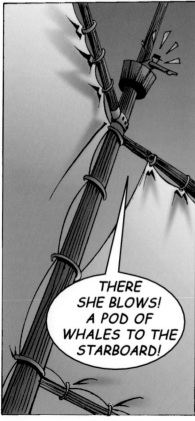

THERE SHE BLOWS! A POD OF WHALES TO THE STARBOARD!

NAY, CAPTAIN!!

MOBY DICK IS NOT THERE!

Sir, I am ready to send out the boats so we can begin the hunt.

The white whale is not there. There is no reason to send out the boats.

Captain, the purpose of this journey is to fill oil barrels. We can't let a pod of whales go.

If we stay here, Moby Dick will move farther away from us.

Sir, the owners of the *Pequod* are counting on a successful expedition. Besides, don't you want to see your harpooners in action? Don't you want to know that they will able to bring down the beast that haunts you?

Very well, Starbuck. I will give the ship one day in this spot. No more. Then we continue the hunt for the white whale.

THE CREW SET OUT TOWARD THE POD OF WHALES AS AHAB WATCHED SILENTLY.

THAT NIGHT, THE CREW BEGAN TO CUT THE BLUBBER OFF THE TWO WHALES THEY HAD KILLED. THEY WORKED QUICKLY BECAUSE CAPTAIN AHAB DEMANDED THAT THE *PEQUOD* BE READY TO SET SAIL AT SUNRISE.

The most evil creature I have ever encountered is out there. He taunts me, Starbuck. He taunts me, and I shall have him. I cannot rest until the white whale is destroyed.

Sir, I have a family back home to support. I cannot afford to go back empty-handed. We will all be denied pay if you continue this hunt for Moby Dick.

I have a family too.

I have a son who knows nothing about me.

But I will have my revenge against that accursed beast.

I *will* raise Moby Dick from the ocean, and I will finally know peace.

He is out there ....

I can *feel* it ....

STARBUCK BEGAN TO FEAR THAT AHAB WOULD GET THE ENTIRE CREW KILLED. HE TRIED TO GET STUBBS TO HELP HIM TAKE THE COMMAND AWAY FROM AHAB.

Our captain can think of nothing but revenge.

We must take control of the *Pequod.*

Don't speak of mutiny to me, Starbuck.

I take my orders from *Ahab.*

STARBUCK WAS UNABLE TO CONVINCE ANYONE TO HELP HIM.

MOST OF THE CREW WAS ANXIOUS TO CLAIM AHAB'S REWARD FOR THE DEATH OF THE WHITE WHALE.

ANOTHER SHIP, DEAD AHEAD!

What is happening?

Another whaling ship is near.

It is a custom to share food and music with its crew. It will lift our spirits.

Moby Dick? Aye! Two days ago. We nearly collided with the brute!

Where, Dowling? Where did you lay your eyes on the monster?

Due north. He's heading toward the icy seas.

You don't seek the white whale?

Aye! That is the nature of our quest!

I look to destroy the beast once and for all!

It is not wise! Moby Dick is not a creature to pursue!

He took the very leg I used to stand on, Dowling! I will revenge myself against the evil creature!

You may as well revenge yourself on the sea that gave him life, Ahab!

If the sea had taken my leg, I would look for a way to destroy it!

Please, come join my crew for a feast! Let me discuss this matter with you!

No. We must be on our way. Starbuck, set sail due north.

Captain, the men could use a break. It is disrespectful to turn down an invitation to another whaling ship. It's ...

You have your orders, Starbuck! Carry them out.

SAMUEL ENDERBY

Goodbye, Ahab! For your sake, I hope you don't find what you're looking for!

Ahab had no right to deny us a break!

Maybe Starbuck is right about our captain!

That'll be enough of that talk! Who are you to question Ahab?

IT WAS ISHMAEL'S TURN TO BE THE LOOKOUT. AS HIS EYES SCANNED THE CALM WAVES, HE THOUGHT ABOUT AHAB. WAS THE CAPTAIN TAKING HIS DESIRE FOR REVENGE TOO FAR?

THEN SUDDENLY, HE SPOTTED MOBY DICK!

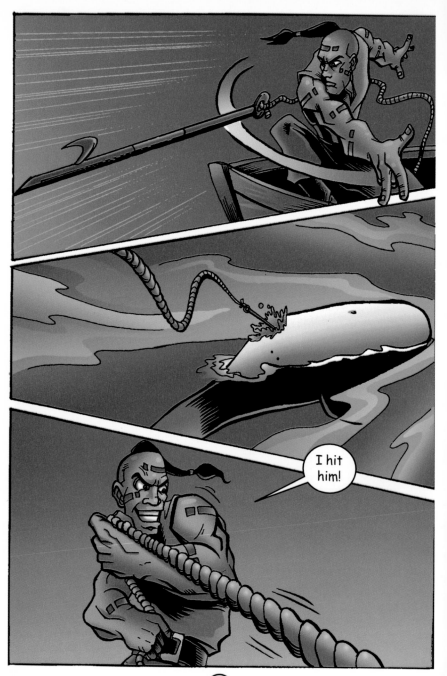

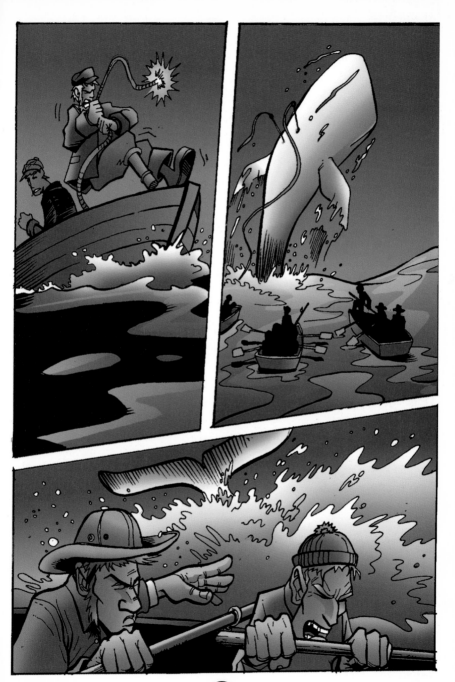

He is submerged, sir. He is gone.

He will resurface! We'll spot him!

He won't need to come up for air for a long time.

He could be miles away by then!

THE CREW RETURNED TO THE PEQUOD, AND AHAB HEADED THE SHIP TOWARD THE NORTH.

Sir, we have spotted a large pod of whales to the west.

We go north, Starbuck. That is where the white whale goes, and that is where I follow.

THE *PEQUOD* FOLLOWED THE TRAIL OF THE WHITE WHALE TO THE ICY WATERS OF THE ARCTIC.

MORE AND MORE OF THE CREW MEMBERS WERE BEGINNING TO QUESTION AHAB'S AUTHORITY.

THE CREW WAS SOON IN FOR EVEN MORE OF A SHOCK. THEY CAME ACROSS ANOTHER SHIP, THE *RACHEL*. THE CAPTAIN'S OWN SON HAD BEEN LOST AT SEA, AND HE BEGGED AHAB TO HELP HIM SEARCH. AHAB REFUSED. HE DIDN'T WANT TO LOSE ANY MORE TIME IN HIS QUEST FOR THE WHITE WHALE.

HOW CAN YOU REFUSE TO HELP ME AHAB? WHAT IF IT WERE YOUR SON LOST AT SEA?

Keep our course.

TO TURN DOWN A DISTRESS CALL WAS THE WORST CRIME A CAPTAIN COULD COMMIT. SOME OF THE CREW BEGAN TO PLOT A TAKEOVER OF THE SHIP.

BUT BEFORE THE CREW COULD TRY TO TAKE OVER THE SHIP, THE *PEQUOD* WAS CAUGHT IN A HORRIBLE STORM.

WE MUST TURN BACK, CAPTAIN!

THIS STORM WILL TEAR THE BOAT APART!

NO!

WE MUST PRESS ON!

AHAB STEERED THE ***PEQUOD*** INTO THE VERY HEART OF THE STORM. MANY THOUGHT THE SHIP WOULD BREAK APART.

THE SUN CAST A BRIGHT LIGHT ON THE DARK SHIP.

See, my men! Fate is with us!

We have crossed ice and typhoon and still this ship continues! The end of our quest is near!

AHAB DOVE AFTER HIM.

YOU'LL NOT ESCAPE ME THIS TIME!

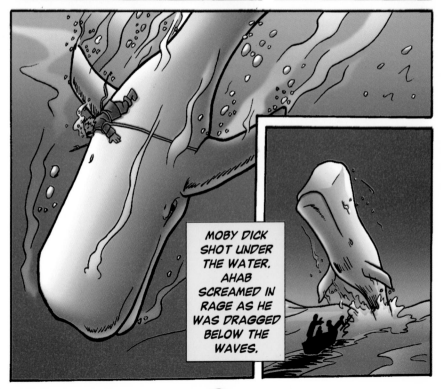

MOBY DICK SHOT UNDER THE WATER. AHAB SCREAMED IN RAGE AS HE WAS DRAGGED BELOW THE WAVES.

ISHMAEL WATCHED IN HORROR AS THE *PEQUOD* AND HER CREW WERE DESTROYED IN FRONT OF HIM.

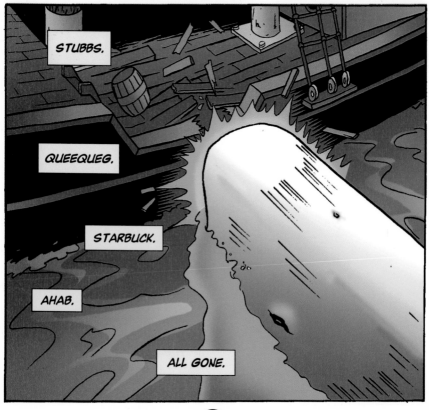

STUBBS.

QUEEQUEG.

STARBUCK.

AHAB.

ALL GONE.

AFTER THE *PEQUOD* AND THE REMAINING CREW WERE DESTROYED, MOBY DICK DISAPPEARED BENEATH THE WATER.

ISHMAEL WAS THE SOLE SURVIVOR.

TWO DAYS PASSED, AND ISHMAEL WAS RESCUED BY THE *RACHEL.* HE RETURNED TO NANTUCKET. IN THE YEARS TO COME, HE WOULD THINK OFTEN ABOUT AHAB AND THE EVENTS ABOARD THE *PEQUOD.*

HE DECIDED, AFTER A TIME, THAT THERE WERE TWO THINGS BEST LEFT ALONE.

THOSE TWO THINGS WERE REVENGE ... AND MOBY DICK!